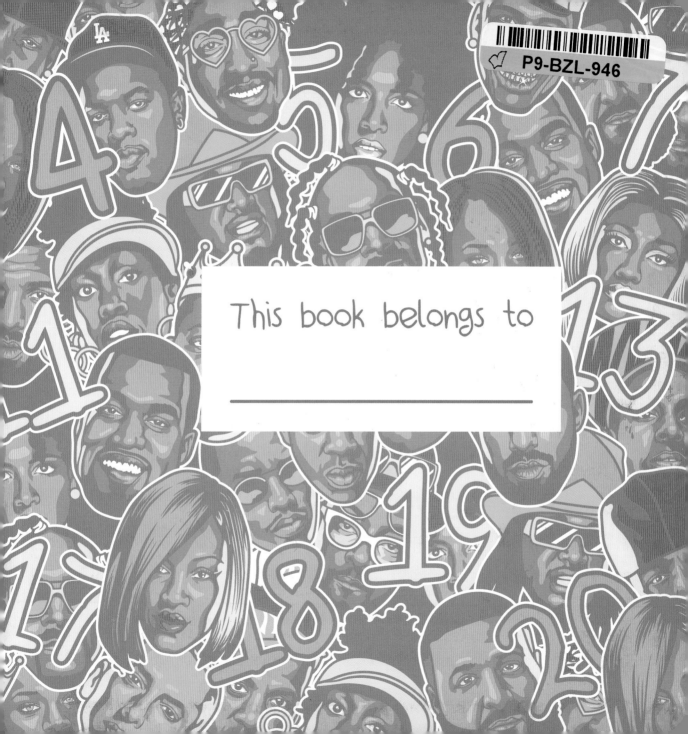

This book belongs to

_____

Dedicated to
Lola Willow

1 2 3
with the
Notorious
B.I.G.

By Jessica Chiha

Illustrations by Alex Lehours

1

Nelly asked the jewellery store to make him
ONE set of grillz

Nicki Minaj has got TWO buns to feed her pet anaconda

Kanye West is trying to keep up with THREE kardashians

Diddy just produced FOUR new hit records

Snoop Dogg dropped his FIVE potatoes like they were hot

Missy Elliott is going to work it with her SIX hoop earrings

Dr. Dre is rocking to some beats on his
SEVEN sets of headphones

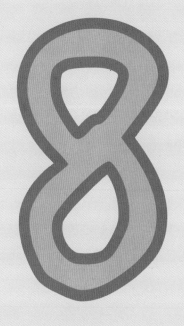

Jay-Z is going to run this town in his
EIGHT hats

Kelis is drinking NINE milkshakes in the yard

The Notorious B.I.G. is playing on his TEN
Super Nintendos and Sega Genesis consoles

Ja Rule is always on time with his
ELEVEN watches

Rihanna is standing under her TWELVE umbrellas now that it is raining more than ever

Drake is waiting for you to call him on his
THIRTEEN cell phones

Eminem ate FOURTEEN bowls of his Mum's spaghetti

Lil Wayne is licking his FIFTEEN lollipops

16

Eve is shaking her SIXTEEN
tambourines

17

will.i.am was given SEVENTEEN
pairs of glasses from his Mama

T-Pain is going to buy EIGHTEEN drinks and take them home with him

19

DJ Khaled found NINETEEN major keys and he likes that

Tupac is looking for some California love
with his TWENTY bandanas